READING CARAVAN

PEPPERMINT FENCE

REVISED EDITION

PAUL A. WITTY

MILDRED HOYT BEBELL

CALIFORNIA STATE SERIES

Published by

CALIFORNIA STATE DEPARTMENT OF EDUCATION

Sacramento, 1969

CONTRIBUTING AUTHORS

PHYLLISS S. ADAMS, *Assistant Professor of Education, University of Denver, Denver, Colorado*

HELEN CHANCELLOR ACHATZ, *Principal, Lowell Elementary School, Englewood, Colorado*

V. JUNE HAAS, *Coordinator, Denver Public Schools, Denver, Colorado*

Illustrated by KELLY OECHSLI

Cover by WINNIE FITCH PHELAN

ACKNOWLEDGMENTS

For permission to reprint copyrighted material, grateful acknowledgment is made to the following publishers, authors, and agents:

Abelard-Schuman Ltd., for "My Puppy," "One Day When It Was Sunny," "Runny Days, Sunny Days," and "Thinking," reprinted from *Runny Days, Sunny Days* by Aileen Fisher, by permission of Abelard-Schuman Ltd., all rights reserved, copyright 1958.

The Better Reading Foundation, Inc., for "Where Is Danny?" adapted from "Robin Was Here" by Ruth S. Redlauer. For "Cubby Bear," adapted from "Cubby Bear's Walk" by Duncan Morrison. These stories first appeared in *Humpty Dumpty's Magazine.*

Dodd, Mead & Company, Inc., for "Mr. Fox and Mr. Rabbit" and "Magpie's Nest," adapted and reprinted by permission of the publisher, from "The Fox and the Rabbit" and "The Magpie's Nest" in *A Child's Book of Stories* by Penrhyn W. Coussens, copyright 1948. For "Nonsense Alphabet," reprinted by permission of Dodd, Mead & Company, Inc., from *The Complete Nonsense Book* by Edward Lear and by permission of the Administrators of Constance S. Esther Rosa Cipelletti Lady Strachie, deceased.

E. P. Dutton & Company, Inc., for "The End," from the book *Now We Are Six* by A. A. Milne, copyright 1927 by E. P. Dutton & Company, Inc., renewal 1955 by A. A. Milne, reprinted by permission of the publishers. For "Happiness," from the book *When We Were Very Young* by A. A. Milne, copyright 1924 by E. P. Dutton & Company, Inc., renewal 1952 by A. A. Milne, reprinted by permission of the publishers. For six lines of "Little Black Bug" by Margaret Wise Brown, from *Another Here and Now Story Book* by Lucy Sprague Mitchell, copyright 1937 by E. P. Dutton & Company, Inc., reprinted by permission of the publishers. For "Weather," copyright 1941 by Marchette Chute, from the book *Around and About* by Marchette Chute. Published 1957 by E. P. Dutton & Company, Inc., and reprinted with their permission.

Steffi Fletcher, for "Little Red Car" by Steffi Fletcher, adapted and reprinted by special permission from *Jack and Jill* © 1960, The Curtis Publishing Company.

Marjorie G. Fribourg, for "Rain," based on the story idea in "Alfred's Rain" by Marjorie G. Fribourg, which first appeared in *Humpty Dumpty's Magazine*.

Le Grand Henderson, for reprinting the adapted form of "What About Willie?" by Le Grand.

Highlights for Children, Inc., for "Little Black Pony," "Ted's Balloon," "Up in a Tree," "The Wiggle-Waggle Cow," and "The Wind's Trick." The ideas in these stories were derived and adapted from similar stories written by Edith Vestal and published in *Highlights for Children:* "The New Owner," copyright 1960; "Sammy's Balloon Came Home," copyright 1959; "What Did Frosty Do for Tom?" copyright 1960; "The Wiggle-Waggle Cow," copyright 1955; and "Did the Wind Play the Trick?" copyright 1957. Likewise, "The Cricket," from a similar story written by Gail Stephenson, "Timothy Why and the Cricket," printed in *Highlights for Children*, copyright 1957. By permission of Highlights for Children, Inc., Columbus, Ohio.

The Instructor, for "I'm a Rocket" by Dorothy M. Wisooker, copyright 1961 by F. A. Owen Publishing Company; reprinted from *The Instructor* by permission.

Leland B. Jacobs, for two verses of "Yellow Bird, Fly" by Leland B. Jacobs.

J. B. Lippincott Company, for "Jonathan" and "To the Shop," from *Picture Rhymes from Foreign Lands* by Rose Fyleman.

Lothrop, Lee & Shepard Company, Inc., for "Winter," by permission of Lothrop, Lee & Shepard Company, Inc., from *Everybody Has Two Eyes* by Jean Jászi.

The Macmillan Company, for one verse of "The Kangaroo," reprinted with permission of the publisher, from *Summer Green* by Elizabeth Coatsworth, copyright 1948 by The Macmillan Company.

Methuen & Company Ltd., for "The End," from *Now We Are Six* by A. A. Milne and for "Happiness," from *When We Were Very Young* by A. A. Milne.

Lilian Moore, for "Bunny Flop and Bunny Hop" and "Snow Boy." These stories were based on the ideas in the stories "White Bunny and Brown Bunny" and "Little Brown Dog and the Snow Boy" by Lilian Moore, which first appeared in *Humpty Dumpty's Magazine*.

William Morrow and Company, Inc., for "Hoppy," adapted from "The Baby Kangaroo That Lived in a Sock," from *True Zoo Stories* by William Bridges, copyright 1948 by William Bridges, by permission of William Morrow and Company, Inc.

Miriam Clark Potter, for the adapted form of "Little Bug and Big Bug" by Miriam Clark Potter.

Whitman Publishing Company, for "Molly and Mops," adapted from *Surprise* by Charims, copyright 1935 by Whitman Publishing Company and used by permission of Whitman Publishing Company.

CONTENTS

You and Me

Down the Road

YOU AND ME

I'm a Rocket

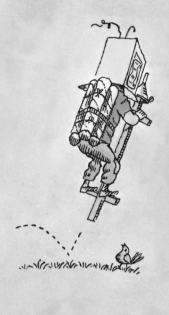

I'm a rocket

Pointing to the moon!

4. . .3. . .2. . .1. . .

Blast off! Zoom!

By Dorothy M. Wisooker

11

Where Is Danny?

"Danny, Danny," said Mother.
"Come here."

"Where is Danny?" said Mother.
"Danny is not here."

"Danny was here," said Mother.
"But where is he now?"

"Danny was here," said Mother.
"And here he is now!"

13

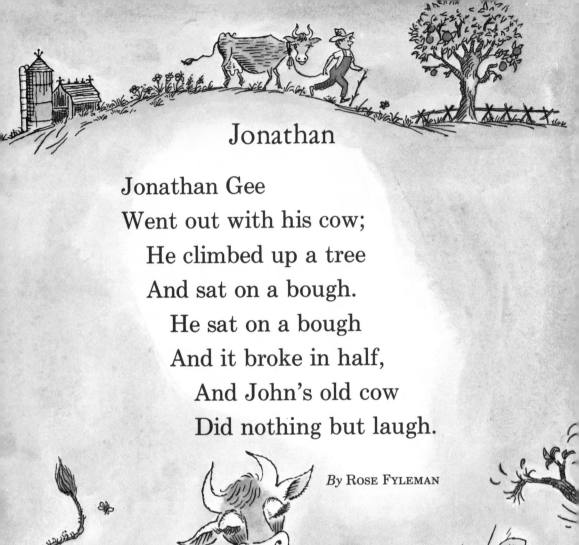

Jonathan

Jonathan Gee
Went out with his cow;
He climbed up a tree
And sat on a bough.
He sat on a bough
And it broke in half,
And John's old cow
Did nothing but laugh.

By ROSE FYLEMAN

The Wiggle-Waggle Cow

"Jill! Jill!" said Danny.
"Come here! Come here!
Come and see the cow."

"Hello!" said Jill.
"Hello, wiggle-waggle cow."

"Look, Jill," said Danny.
"Look at the wiggle-waggle cow.
She wants to come in."

Wiggle-waggle!
The cow's head went up and down.

"Oh, Mother!" said Danny.
"A cow is in the house.
A wiggle-waggle cow!"

"What!" said Mother.

"Yes, Mother," said Jill.
"A wiggle-waggle cow!
She wants to play."

Wiggle-waggle!
The cow's head went up and down.

Off came the cow's head.
And up jumped Ted.

"Ha, ha!" said Ted.
"I was the wiggle-waggle cow."

Up in a Tree

"Hello, Ted," said Jill.
"Come and climb the tree."

"Hello, Ted," said Danny.
"Come on!"

Up the big tree went Jill.
Up the big tree went Danny.

19

Ted wanted to climb the tree.
But he was afraid.
"I will look for my kitten," he said.

"Where is my kitten?" said Ted.
He looked and looked.

Something said, "Mee-ow."
Something up in a tree.

Ted looked up.
"My kitten!" he said.
"Come down, little kitten!"

. The kitten said, "Mee-ow."
But she did not come down.

"Jill! Danny!" said Ted.
"Come and help me."

But Jill and Danny did not come.

"My kitten is afraid!" said Ted.
And up the tree he went.

Down Ted came with the kitten.
"Oh, little kitten!" said Ted.
"I was not afraid!
I was not afraid!
I like to climb trees now."

Ted's Balloon

Ted wanted to climb the tree.
"But what can I do?" he said.
"I can not climb with a balloon.
What can I do with it?"

Ted saw the car.
"My balloon can go here," he said.
"Now I can climb the tree."

23

Danny came to see Ted.
"I have my red balloon," said Danny.
"Get your balloon."

Ted climbed down the tree.
He went to get the balloon.

"Danny!" said Ted.
"My balloon is not here.
But it will come home."

"It will not come home," said Danny.

"Oh, yes, it will," said Ted.

Jill came to see Ted.
"Oh, Ted!" said Jill.
"I have my orange balloon.
Where is your green balloon?"

"It is not here," said Ted.
"Oh! Here it comes now!
See, Danny, it did come home."

"Where? Where?" said Danny.
"I do not see your green balloon."

"Look at the car," said Ted.

"Ha, ha," said Danny.
"Now I see your balloon.
It did go away.
It did come home.
It was on the car."

The End

When I was One,
I had just begun.

When I was Two,
I was nearly new.

When I was Three,
I was hardly Me.

When I was Four,
I was not much more.

When I was Five,
I was just alive.

But now I am Six, I'm as clever as clever.
So I think I'll be six now for ever and ever.

By A. A. Milne

27

Where?

1. Where was the balloon?

2. Where was the kitten?

3. Where was Danny?

4. Where was Ted?

DOWN THE ROAD

Thinking

Wouldn't it be funny
If somehow I could shrink
And turn into a bunny
And learn what bunnies think?

By AILEEN FISHER

Bunny Flop and Bunny Hop

"I will go away," said Bunny Flop.
"I will see what I can see."
Up the road he went.

"I will go away, too," said Bunny Hop.
"I will see what I can see."
Down the road he went.

Bunny Flop went up the road.
On and on he went.
He looked and looked and looked.

"Oh, my!" he said.
"Up and down!
Up and down!
All things go up and down."

Bunny Flop went home.

Bunny Hop went down the road.
On and on he went.
He looked and looked and looked.

"My! My!" he said.
"What do I see?
All things go around.
Around and around!"

Bunny Hop went home, too.

"Oh, Mother," said Bunny Flop.
"I saw things go up and down.
All things go up and down."

"No!" said Bunny Hop.
"I saw things go around and around.
All things go around and around."

"Up and down!" said Bunny Flop.

"Around and around!" said Bunny Hop.

Mother Bunny looked at Bunny Hop.
"Bunny Hop," she said.
"Some things go around and around."

Mother Bunny looked at Bunny Flop.
"Bunny Flop," she said.
"Some things go up and down."

"Oh!" said Bunny Hop.

"Oh!" said Bunny Flop.

And they went off to play.

Yellow Bird, Fly

Yellow bird, yellow bird,
Blink your eye,
Yellow bird, yellow bird,
Fly, fly, fly.

Yellow bird, yellow bird,
Dip your wing,
Yellow bird, yellow bird,
Sing, sing, sing.

By LELAND B. JACOBS

Little Red Car

Down the road went Little Red Car.
Chug-chug-chug-chug!

"Oh," said Little Red Car.
"This is not what I want to do.
I want to fly."

Chug-chug-chug-chug!
Little Red Car saw a mouse.

"Oh, Mouse, Mouse!" he said.
"Can you fly?"

"No, I can not fly," said the mouse.
"But I can run."

"I want to fly," said Little Red Car.

Chug-chug, on and on.
Little Red Car saw a squirrel.

"Oh, Squirrel, Squirrel!" he said.
"Can you fly?"

"No, I can not fly," said the squirrel.
"But I can jump."

"I want to fly," said Little Red Car.

Chug-chug, on and on.
Little Red Car saw a bird.

"Little Bird, Little Bird," he said.
"Can you fly?"

"Oh, yes, I can fly," said the bird.
"I fly with my wings."

"Wings! Wings!" said Little Red Car.
"Where can I get wings?"

Chug-chug, on and on.
Little Red Car saw a man.

"Man, Man," he said.
"I want to fly.
But I have no wings.
Where can I get wings?"

"Oh!" said the man.
"I make wings for airplanes.
I will make wings for you.
Little red wings!"

Chug-chug, zoom-m, zoom-m!
Up, up went Little Red Car.
Little Red Car looked around.
He saw the little bird.

"Look!" said Little Red Car.
"I can fly! I can fly!
I can fly with you, Little Bird!"

And up he went with the little bird.
Zoom-m, zoom-m, zoom-m-m-m!

42

Little Bug and Big Bug

Little Bug had a house.
It was a little house.

Little Bug had a little chair.
The little chair was blue.

Little Bug had a little table.
The little table was green.

Little Bug had a little bed.
And it was red.

Little Bug went down the road.
Little Bug came home.
And who was in the house?
Big Bug!

"Hello," said Big Bug.
"I want your little red bed.
I will take it home with me."

"Oh, Big Bug," said Little Bug.
"Take my blue chair.
Take my green table.
But not my little red bed."

"No, no," said Big Bug.
"I do not want your blue chair.
I do not want your green table.
I do want your little red bed."

"No," said Little Bug.
"You can not have my red bed.
You are too big for my red bed.
Get on it and you will see."

"Oh," said Big Bug.
"Your bed is too little for me."

"Oh, Big Bug," said Little Bug.
"You are not too big to play with.
Will you play with me?"

"Oh, yes," said Big Bug.

Little Bug was happy now.
He had a little blue chair.
He had a little green table.
He had a little red bed.
And he had a good friend.

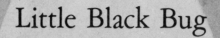

Little Black Bug

Little black bug,
Little black bug,
Where have you been?
I've been under the rug,
Said little black bug.
Bug-ug-ug-ug.

By MARGARET WISE BROWN

49

What?

1. What was red?

2. What was blue?

3. What was green?

4. What went up and down?

5. What went around and around?

6. What was little?

7. What was big?

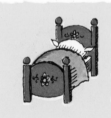

DAYS
AND
DAYS

Winter

See the far hills white with snow
See the river black below
See the bare trees
See the land—
Wearing mittens
Like my hand.

By JEAN JÁSZI

Snow Boy

Down,
  down,
    down.
White snow.
White snow.

Snow on the houses.
Snow on the trees.
Snow on the roads.
Down, down, it came.

Little Dog came out to play.

"Bow-wow-wow," he said.
"A snow boy! A snow boy!
Bow-wow-wow."

"Hello, Snow Boy," he said.
"I want to play with you."

Little Dog was happy.

He jumped up and down.

He went around and around Snow Boy.

Little Dog played and played.

"Snow Boy," he said.

"You are my friend.

I like to play with you.

But I have to stop now."

And Little Dog went home.

The sun was out.

Little Dog came out to play.

He wanted to play with his friend.

"Where is Snow Boy?" he said.

"I want to play with Snow Boy."

Little Dog looked all around.

No snow! No Snow Boy!

Little Dog went home.

Where was Snow Boy?

Happiness

John had
Great Big
Waterproof
Boots on;
John had a
Great Big
Waterproof
Hat;
John had a
Great Big
Waterproof
Mackintosh—
And that
(Said John)
Is
That.

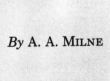

By A. A. MILNE

57

Rain

Alfred jumped up.

He looked out.

He looked all around.

"The sun is out," said Alfred.

But Alfred was not happy.

He had a raincoat.

And he wanted it to rain.

Alfred jumped up.
"Will it rain?" said Alfred.

He went to the TV.
Click!
But the TV man said, "No rain."

Alfred was not happy.
He had a raincoat.
And he wanted it to rain.

Alfred went out.

Yang! Yang! Yang!
Weeeeeee!
The firemen jumped out.
Swooosh went the water!

"Look at the water!" said Alfred.
"Look at the raincoats!"

Alfred went home.
On went his raincoat.
Then Alfred played fireman.

"Yang! Yang! Yang!" said Alfred.
"Weeeeeee!"

"Look at the water!" said Alfred.
"Look at my raincoat!"

Alfred liked what he saw.
But he wanted it to rain.

Alfred jumped up.
He looked out.
He looked all around.
Rain! Rain! Rain!

"Wheeeee!" said Alfred.
On went his raincoat.
Out went Alfred.

Alfred was happy.
Rain! Rain! Rain!

The Wind's Trick

The wind said,
   "O-o-o-oh!
   I like to play.
   I play tricks all day."

"Oh, Danny," said Ted.
"The wind can play tricks."

The wind said,
 "O-o-o-oh!
 I like to play.
 I play tricks all day.
 I blow caps away."

"Not my red cap!" said Ted.

"Not my red cap!" said Danny.

The wind said,
  "O-o-o-oh!
  I will blow.
  I will blow your cap away."

Away went Danny's cap.
Up, up, up it went.

Away went Ted's cap, too.
Danny did not see it go up.

Danny ran and ran.
Down came a red cap.
Danny ran to get it.

Danny saw Ted.
"Look, Ted," he said.
"This cap is too big!"

"Oh, Danny," said Ted.
"This cap is too little.
You have my red cap.
I have your red cap.
The wind did play a trick!"

Weather

It is a windy day.
The water's white with spray.
And pretty soon, if this keeps up,
The world will blow away.

By MARCHETTE CHUTE

One Day When It Was Sunny

I saw my picture on the road
One day when it was sunny.
It stretched along in front of me,
Big and black and funny,
And it was taller than I'm tall
And ran when I was runny,
And when I held my hands for ears
It turned into . . . a BUNNY.

By AILEEN FISHER

Cubby Bear

Cubby Bear.   Mother! Mother!
The sun is out.
I want to go for a walk.

Mother Bear.   We can all go.
We can go on a picnic.

Cubby Bear.   A picnic! A picnic!
                I like picnics!

Mother Bear.   Good, Cubby.
                You can help.

Daddy Bear.   Come with me, Cubby.
                We can help Mother.

Daddy Bear.	Cubby, you can run.
	Mother and I will walk.
Mother Bear.	Yes, Cubby, go on.
	Run to the big tree.
Cubby Bear.	Come on, Mother.
	Come on, Daddy.

Cubby Bear.   Daddy! Mother!
Help! Help!

Daddy Bear.   What is it, Cubby?
What is it?

Mother Bear.   What is it, Cubby?

Cubby Bear.   Oh, Daddy!
Oh, Mother!
Something is behind me!

Daddy Bear.   Grr-rrr-rrr!
               Where is it?

Mother Bear.   Grr-rrr-rrr!
               Where is it?

Cubby Bear.   Here, Daddy!
               Here, Mother!
               Here it is.

Mother Bear.   Oh, Cubby Bear!
Look behind Daddy!
Something is there.

Daddy Bear.   And look behind Mother!
Something is there, too.

Cubby Bear.   Oh! Now I see what it is.

Runny Days, Sunny Days

Runny days, sunny days,
Summertime or fall,
Blowy days, snowy days—
Seems I like them all!

By AILEEN FISHER

What Did It Do?

1. What did the wind do?

2. What did the sun do?

3. What did the rain do?

4. What did the snow do?

The sun did this, too.

FRIENDS

The Cricket

Timothy had a cricket.
He had it in his pocket.

"Oh," Timothy said.
"A cricket will not like my pocket.
I will take my cricket out."

He looked in his pocket.
"Where is my cricket?" he said.

Timothy took out a red car.

He took out a blue balloon.

He took out a green airplane.

He took out a little white box.

But no cricket.

No cricket at all!

Timothy looked for his cricket.

Then something said, "Chir-r-rup!"
And there was a cricket!
It was black.
It jumped.

"It is my cricket!" said Timothy.

Timothy took the little white box.
"This is your home now," he said.
In went the cricket.

Timothy had a cricket.
But not in his pocket!

My Puppy

On any day of the year,
At any time of the moon,
At any hour of the day,
I can't see my puppy too soon.

By AILEEN FISHER

Molly and Mops

"Mops," said Molly.
"I want to have a birthday party.
Danny and Ted will come.
Timothy and Jill will come.
And I want you to come, too."

Mops looked up at Molly.
"Bow-wow-wow," said Mops.

One day Molly jumped out of bed.
"Mops! Mops!" she said.
"Where are you?
This is my birthday."

But Mops did not come.

Molly looked and looked.
But no Mops!

It was time for the party.

Danny and Ted came.
Timothy and Jill came, too.

"Happy birthday, Molly," they said.
"Here is something for you."

But Molly was not happy.
Mops was not there.

Mops came out of the house.
"Bow-wow-wow," she said.

"Mops! Mops!" said Molly.
"Come to my birthday party."

But Mops did not go to Molly.
Mops said, "Bow-wow-wow!"
She looked at the house.
And in she went.
In went Molly, too.

There was Molly's birthday surprise!

The Kangaroo

It is a curious thing that you
Don't wish to be a kangaroo,
To hop hop hop
And never stop
The whole day long and the
whole night, too!

By ELIZABETH COATSWORTH

Hoppy

Hoppy was in the zoo.
Alfred went to see Hoppy.
Vicky went, too.

Vicky looked and looked at Hoppy.
"Oh, Alfred!" said Vicky.
"Look at Hoppy's home.
It is his mother's pocket!"

Just then the zoo man took Hoppy.
A man took Hoppy's mother away.

"What can I do?" said the zoo man.
"I have to have a pocket for Hoppy.
His mother had to go away for a day."

"I know! I know!" said Vicky.
"Here is a pocket for Hoppy."

"Look at Hoppy!" said Alfred.
"He likes his pocket."

"Yes," said the zoo man.
"And he likes Vicky, too."

Hoppy was in his pocket.
He was happy now.
He had a home.
A pocket for a home!

To the Shop

I have a little pony
Rising four years old,
His shoes are made of silver,
His bit is made of gold.

Into town I'll send him
To fetch a great big sack
Of tea and sugar-candy
For Mary and for Jack.

By ROSE FYLEMAN

Little Black Pony

Ted liked Mr. Green.
He liked Mr. Green's black pony.
He liked to ride Little Black Pony.

"Ted," said Mr. Green one day.
"Little Black Pony is going away."

"Going away!" said Ted.
"Oh, Little Black Pony!
Then I can not ride you.
What will I do?"

Ted went home.
He was not happy.

One day Mother said, "Look, Ted.
Look down the road.
You will see a surprise."

Ted did look.
He saw Timothy with an airplane.
But that was not a surprise.
He saw Jill with an orange.
But that was not a surprise.

Then Ted saw Mr. Green.
Little Black Pony was with Mr. Green.

"Hello, Mr. Green," said Ted.
"Where is Little Black Pony going?"

"To his home," said Mr. Green.
"And here it is."

"But this is my home," said Ted.

"Yes," said Mr. Green.
"It is his home, too."

"Oh!" said Ted.
"Then Little Black Pony is for me.
What a good surprise!"

What About Willie?

One time there was rain, rain, rain.
And out in the rain was Willie.
Willie was a little kitten.
He wanted a home.

There was a green house by a brook.
And in the house was Tommy.
Tommy was a little boy.
He wanted a kitten.
An orange and black and white kitten.
Just like Willie!

Willie was out in the rain.
And he went on and on.
He wanted a home.

Willie saw a man and said, "Mee-ow."

But the man was Mr. Greeble.
He did not like kittens at all.

"S-s-scat!" said Mr. Greeble.

And Willie did.

Willie came to a white house.

Mrs. Riffles went in.

And so did Willie!

Willie went up,

up,

up.

And he came to a bed.

Mrs. Riffles came up.

There was Willie!

"S-s-scat!" said Mrs. Riffles.

And Willie did.

Willie came to a little red house.
Willie liked it.
He said, "Mee-ow."
But no one came.
So Willie went in.

Then something went, "Wo-o-of!"

Willie was in the dog house!
But in no time he was out.

Willie was out in the rain again.

Willie came to a green house.

It was the green house by a brook.

Willie said, "Mee-ow."

But no one came.

So Willie went to the brook.

There was a big catfish.

And there was a fishline.

"S-snap!" went the catfish.

He had the fishline.

"Mee-ow!" went Willie.

He had the fishline, too.

Willie pulled.

So did the catfish.

And there was Willie in the brook!

"Mee-ow!" said Willie.

And out of the house came Tommy.

Tommy pulled.

The catfish pulled.

Willie pulled.

They all pulled.

Then Tommy pulled again.

And up came Willie and the catfish.

"Aw!" said Tommy.
"An orange and black and white kitten.
Just what I wanted!"

And what about Willie?
Willie had catfish to eat.
And Willie had a home
        in the green house
                by a brook
                        with Tommy.

Who Am I?

1. I am orange and black and white.
   Who am I?

2. I have a pocket for a home.
   Who am I?

3. I have a home with Timothy.
   Who am I?

4. I had a surprise for Molly.
   Who am I?

5. I have a little box for a home.
   Who am I?

Hoppy

Little Black Pony

the kitten

Mops

the cricket

A STORY
TO TELL

Henny-Penny

Henny-Penny wanted something to eat.

She looked and looked.

Something came down—pl-o-p!

"Oh," said Henny-Penny.
"The sky is falling!
I am going to tell the King."

And away she went.

Henny-Penny went on and on.
She came to Cocky-Locky.

"Where are you going?"
said Cocky-Locky.

"Oh, Cocky-Locky!"
said Henny-Penny.
   "The sky is falling!
I am going to tell the King."

"I will go with you,"
said Cocky-Locky.

They went on and on and on.
They came to Ducky-Lucky.

"Where are you going?"
said Ducky-Lucky.

"Oh, Ducky-Lucky!"
said Henny-Penny and Cocky-Locky.
"The sky is falling!
We are going to tell the King."

"I will go with you,"
said Ducky-Lucky.

They went on and on and on.
They came to Goosey-Loosey.

"Where are you going?"
said Goosey-Loosey.

"Oh, Goosey-Loosey!"
said Henny-Penny and Cocky-Locky
and Ducky-Lucky.
   "The sky is falling!
We are going to tell the King."

   "I will go with you,"
said Goosey-Loosey.

They went on and on and on.
They came to Turkey-Lurkey.

"Where are you going?"
said Turkey-Lurkey.

"Oh, Turkey-Lurkey!"
said Henny-Penny and Cocky-Locky
and Ducky-Lucky and Goosey-Loosey.
"The sky is falling!
We are going to tell the King."

"I will go with you,"
said Turkey-Lurkey.

They went on and on and on.
They came to Foxy-Loxy.

"Where are you going?"
said Foxy-Loxy.

"Foxy-Loxy! Foxy-Loxy!"
said Henny-Penny and Cocky-Locky
and Ducky-Lucky and Goosey-Loosey
and Turkey-Lurkey.
   "The sky is falling!
   We are going to tell the King."

"Come with me," said Foxy-Loxy.
"I know how to get there."

They went on and on and on.
Then they came to Foxy-Loxy's home.

S-snap! Off went Turkey-Lurkey's head.
S-snap! Off went Goosey-Loosey's head.
S-snap! Off went Ducky-Lucky's head.

"Go home, Henny-Penny, go home!"
said Cocky-Locky.
Then—s-snap!
Off went Cocky-Locky's head.

Henny-Penny ran home.
She did not tell the King
the sky was falling.

Magpie's Nest

Some birds did not know how
to make nests.
But Magpie did!
The birds went to see Magpie.

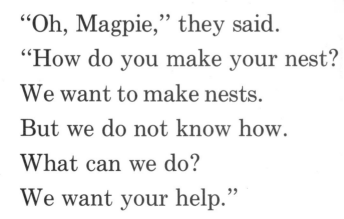

"Oh, Magpie," they said.
"How do you make your nest?
We want to make nests.
But we do not know how.
What can we do?
We want your help."

Magpie said, "Oh!
I will help you.
Watch me make a nest.
Then you will know how."

"Oh, yes," said Red Bird.
"You make a good nest.
Little birds like your nest.
We will watch you make a nest.
Then we will know how."

Magpie said, "First, you do this."

"Oh, yes," said Blue Bird.
"We know how to do that."

"Next, you do this," said Magpie.

"Yes, yes," said Black Bird.
"We know how to do that.
Go on, Magpie."

"Next, you do this," said Magpie.

"Yes, yes, yes," said Red Bird.
"We know how to do that.
Go on, go on, Magpie."

Magpie looked at the birds.
She said, "I will not go on.
You know how.
Go and make your nests."

The birds went home.

The birds worked and worked.
They did all the things
they had watched Magpie do.

But they did not know what
to do next.

To this day, the birds
make nests like this.

They do not know what to do next!

Sing a Song of Sixpence

Sing a song of sixpence,
    A pocket full of rye;
Four-and-twenty blackbirds
    Baked in a pie!

When the pie was opened,
    The birds began to sing;
Was not that a dainty dish
    To set before the king?

The king was in his counting-house
Counting out his money;
The queen was in the parlor,
Eating bread and honey.

The maid was in the garden,
Hanging out the clothes,
When down came a blackbird
And snapped off her nose.

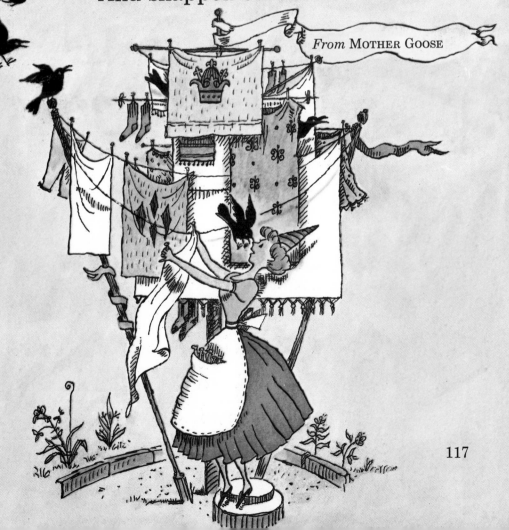

From MOTHER GOOSE

117

Mr. Fox and Mr. Rabbit

Mr. Rabbit was happy.
The sun was out.
And he had no work to do.

Mr. Rabbit looked down the road.
"Here comes Mr. Fox," he said.
"Mr. Fox likes to eat rabbits.
I will play a trick on Mr. Fox."

Mr. Rabbit went pl-o-p
down in the road.

He said, "Mr. Fox will see me
in the road.

Then he will want to eat me.

But I will jump up
and run away.

Mr. Fox is not going to eat
this rabbit.

Ha! Ha! This is a good trick!"

Down the road came Mr. Fox.

Mr. Fox saw a rabbit
in the road.
"My! My!" said Mr. Fox.
"I will have a rabbit to eat."

Mr. Rabbit jumped up and ran.
"Ha! Ha! Ha!" he said.

Mr. Fox ran, too.
"Oh, it is you," said Mr. Fox.
"You played a trick on me.
Now I will play a trick on you.
I will eat you!"

Mr. Rabbit came to his house.
In he jumped!

Mr. Rabbit said, "Ha! Ha! Ha!
You can not get me now.
You can not eat me!"

Mr. Fox said, "One day
I will come for you.
Then I will eat you!"
And Mr. Fox went home.

Mr. Rabbit said, "Ha! Ha! Ha!"

The Three Little Kittens

Three little kittens
They lost their mittens,
   And they began to cry,
"Oh, mother dear,
We sadly fear
   Our mittens we have lost."
"What! Lost your mittens!
You naughty kittens!
   Then you shall have no pie."
   "Mee-ow, mee-ow, mee-ow."
   "No, you shall have no pie."

The three little kittens
They found their mittens,
   And they began to cry,
"Oh, mother dear,
See here, see here,
   Our mittens we have found."
"Put on your mittens,
You silly kittens,
   And you shall have some pie."
"Purr-r, purr-r, purr-r,
   Oh, let us have some pie."

123

The three little kittens
Put on their mittens
    And soon ate up the pie;
"Oh, mother dear,
We greatly fear
    Our mittens we have soiled."
"What! Soiled your mittens!
You naughty kittens!"
    Then they began to sigh,
    "Mee-ow, mee-ow, mee-ow."
    Then they began to sigh.

The three little kittens
They washed their mittens,
   And hung them out to dry;
"Oh! mother dear,
Do you not hear,
   Our mittens we have washed?"
"What! Washed your mittens!
Then you're good kittens,
   But I smell a rat close by."
   "Mee-ow, mee-ow, mee-ow,
   We smell a rat close by."

From MOTHER GOOSE

The Story of
the Three Little Pigs

One time there was a Mother Pig
and Three Little Pigs.

One day Mother Pig said,
"Little Pigs, Little Pigs.
It is time for you to go away."

"Oh, yes," said the Three Little Pigs.
"We want to see what we can see."

And away they went.

The first Little Pig saw a man
with some straw.

"Oh, Man," said the Little Pig.
"I want some straw
to make me a house."

"Here it is," said the man.

The first Little Pig made a house
of straw.

The next Little Pig saw a man
with some sticks.

"Oh, Man," said the Little Pig.
"I want some sticks
to make me a house."

"Here they are," said the man.

That Little Pig made a house
of sticks.

The next Little Pig saw a man
with some bricks.

"Oh, Man," said the Little Pig.
"I want some bricks
to make me a house."

"Here they are," said the man.

That Little Pig made a house
of bricks.

The Wolf came to the house of straw.
He said, "Little Pig, Little Pig!
I want to come in."

The Little Pig said, "No, no, no,
by my chinny-chin-chin!"

The Wolf said, "I will huff and puff,
and I will blow your house in."

He huffed and he puffed,
and he did blow the house in.

But the Little Pig had run
to the house of sticks.

The Wolf came to the house of sticks.
He said, "Little Pigs, Little Pigs!
I want to come in."

The Little Pigs said, "No, no, no,
by my chinny-chin-chin!"

The Wolf said, "I will huff and puff,
and I will blow your house in."

He huffed and he puffed,
and he did blow the house in.

But the Little Pigs had run
to the house of bricks.

The Wolf came to the house of bricks.
He said, "Little Pigs, Little Pigs!
I want to come in."

The Little Pigs said, "No, no, no,
by my chinny-chin-chin!"

The Wolf said, "I will huff and puff,
and I will blow your house in."

He huffed and he puffed
and he puffed and he huffed.
But he did not blow the house in.

"Grrr-rrr-rrr!" said the Wolf.
"I am going to eat you!
This time I will come down
and get you."

And down he went.

"Ha! Ha! Ha!" said the Three Little
Pigs.
"We are going to eat you!"

And they did.

Who Said It?

1. "The sky is falling!"

2. "No, no, no,
   by my chinny-chin-chin!"

3. "Go and make your nests."

4. "I will play a trick on Mr. Fox."

5. "I will huff and puff,
   and I will blow your house in."

6. "Go home, Henny-Penny, go home!"

Wolf

Three Little Pigs

Henny-Penny

Cocky-Locky

Magpie

Mr. Rabbit

NONSENSE ALPHABET

was once an apple-pie,

    Pidy,
    Widy,
    Tidy,
    Pidy,
  Nice insidy,
  Apple-pie!

was once a little bear,

    Beary,
    Wary,
    Hairy,
    Beary,
  Taky cary,
  Little bear!

C was once a little cake,
Caky,
Baky,
Maky,
Caky,
Taky caky,
Little cake!

D was once a little doll,
Dolly,
Molly,
Polly,
Nolly,
Nursy dolly,
Little doll!

E was once a little eel,
    Eely,
    Weely,
    Peely,
    Eely,
    Twirly, tweely,
Little eel!

F was once a little fish,
    Fishy,
    Wishy,
    Squishy,
    Fishy,
    In a dishy,
    Little fish!

138

G was once a little goose,
       Goosy,
       Moosy,
       Boosey,
       Goosey,
       Waddly-woosy,
       Little goose!

H was once a little hen,
       Henny,
       Chenny,
       Tenny,
       Henny.
       Eggsy-any,
       Little hen?

was once a bottle of ink,

> Inky,
> Dinky,
> Thinky,
> Inky,
> Blacky minky,
> Bottle of ink!

was once a jar of jam,

> Jammy,
> Mammy,
> Clammy,
> Jammy,
> Sweety, swammy,
> Jar of jam!

 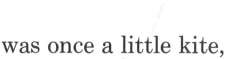  was once a little kite,

Kity,

Whity,

Flighty,

Kity,

Out of sighty,

Little kite!

 was once a little lark,

Larky,

Marky,

Harky,

Larky,

In the parky,

Little lark!

M was once a little mouse,
Mousy,
Bousy,
Sousy,
Mousy,
In the housy,
Little mouse!

N was once a little needle,
Needly,
Tweedly,
Threedly,
Needly,
Wisky, wheedly,
Little needle!

142

 was once a little owl,

> Owly,
> Prowly,
> Howly,
> Owly,
> Browny fowly,
> Little owl!

 was once a little pump,

> Pumpy,
> Slumpy,
> Flumpy,
> Pumpy,
> Dumpy, thumpy,
> Little pump!

Q was once a little quail,
    Quaily,
    Faily,
    Daily,
    Quaily,
    Stumpy-taily,
    Little quail!

R was once a little rose,
    Rosy,
    Posy,
    Nosy,
    Rosy,
    Blows-y, grows-y,
    Little rose!

144

S was once a little shrimp,
       Shrimpy,
       Nimpy,
       Flimpy,
       Shrimpy.
Jumpy, jimpy,
Little shrimp!

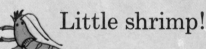

T was once a little thrush,
       Thrushy,
       Hushy,
       Bushy,
       Thrushy,
Flitty, flushy,
Little thrush!

145

U was once a little urn,
Urny,
Burny,
Turny,
Urny,
Bubbly, burny,
Little urn!

V was once a little vine,
Viny,
Winy,
Twiny,
Viny,
Twisty-twiny,
Little vine!

was once a whale,
> Whaly,
> Scaly,
> Shaly,
> Whaly,
> Tumbly-taily,
> Mighty whale!

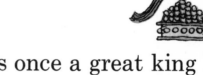

was once a great king Xerxes,
> Xerxy,
> Perxy,
> Turxy,
> Xerxy,
> Linxy, lurxy,
> Great King Xerxes!

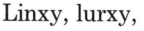

Y was once a little yew,
        Yewdy,
        Fewdy,
        Crudy,
        Yewdy,
Growdy, grewdy,
Little yew!

Z was once a piece of zinc,
        Tinky,
        Winky,
        Blinky,
        Tinky,
Tinkly minky,
Piece of zinc!

By Edward Lear

148

Which?

1. Which tells about A?
   Say that part.

2. Which tells about B?
   Say that part.

3. Which tells about C?
   Say that part.

4. Which part do you like best?
   Why do you like it?

5. Say the part that
   you like best.

149

Picture Dictionary

A a   airplanes

Alfred

B b   balloon

bed

Big Bug

brook

Bunny Flop

Bunny Hop

C c

car

catfish

chair

Cocky-Locky

cow

Cubby Bear

D d

Daddy Bear

Danny

Ducky-Lucky

E e

eel

F f

fishline

Foxy-Loxy

G g

Goosey-Loosey

H h

head

Henny-Penny

Hoppy

house

I i ink

J j Jill

K k King

kitten

L l Little Black Pony

Little Bug

Little Dog

Little Red Car

M m

Magpie

Molly

Mops

Mother Bear

Mr. Fox

Mr. Rabbit

N n

nest

O o

orange

P p

party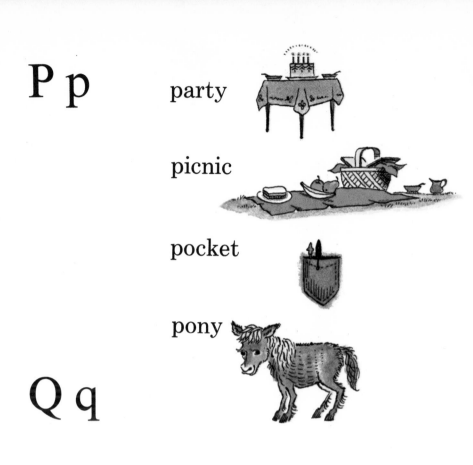

picnic

pocket

pony

Q q

R r

rabbits

rain

raincoat

road

S s   Snow Boy

sun

T t   table

Ted

Three Little Pigs

Timothy

Tommy

tree

Turkey-Lurkey

U u

V v   Vicky

W w   Willie

wings

Wolf

X x

Y y

Z z   zoo